Please return to
the desk of :
*Mrs. Smith*

GRADE

**1**

# WORKBOOK

ISBN 0-439-52414-8

SCHOLASTIC, FLUENCY FORMULA, and associated logos and designs are trademarks and/or
registered trademarks of Scholastic Inc.

1 2 3 4 5 6 7 8 9 10      40      12 11 10 09 08 07 06 05 04 03

# Table of Contents

## Unit 1

Reading Log ........................... 3
The Alphabet Song ...................... 4
I See ................................. 7
Pop! Pop! Popcorn! ..................... 10
Sam Sat ............................... 13

## Unit 2

Reading Log ........................... 16
The Alphabet Forward
and Backwards ......................... 17
A Bug in a Jug ........................ 21
I See a Cat ........................... 24
This Is the Way We Go to School ....... 27

## Unit 3

Reading Log ........................... 30
Crab Jab! ............................. 31
A Lot on Top .......................... 34
Will It Fit? .......................... 36
Pigs at Bat ........................... 39

## Unit 4

Reading Log ........................... 42
New Frog in the Pond .................. 43
Bunny Hop ............................. 46
My Hand Says Hello .................... 49
The Red Hen ........................... 52

## Unit 5

Reading Log ........................... 55
Max's Pet ............................. 56
Big Ben and His Ox .................... 59
The Red Sled .......................... 62
See a Zig-Zag Man ..................... 64

## Unit 6

Reading Log ........................... 67
I Made a Cake ......................... 68
The Cat and the Rat ................... 71
The Pancake Man ....................... 74
Meet Stan ............................. 77

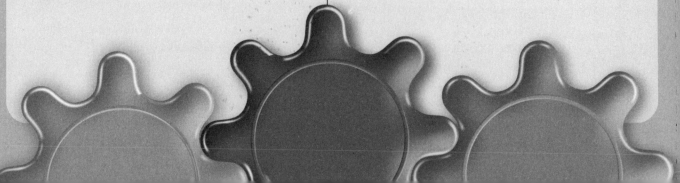

# Books I Read

| Book Title | Rating |
|---|---|
| **1.** | |
| **2.** | |
| **3.** | |
| **4.** | |
| **5.** | |

# The Alphabet Song

7   A - B - C - D - E - F - G,

16   H - I - J - K - L - M - N - O - P,

19   Q - R - S,

22   T - U - V,

24   W - X,

27   Y and Z.

32   Now I know my ABCs.

39   Next time won't you sing with me?

**Connect the Dots!**

**Write the missing small letters on the lines.**

**1**   a \_\_\_\_ c d \_\_\_\_

**2**   m \_\_\_\_ \_\_\_\_ p q

**3**   \_\_\_\_ j k \_\_\_\_ m

**4**   r \_\_\_\_ \_\_\_\_ \_\_\_\_ v

**Write the missing capital letters on the lines.**

**5**   C \_\_\_\_ E \_\_\_\_ G

**6**   \_\_\_\_ I \_\_\_\_ K L

**7**   \_\_\_\_ N O P \_\_\_\_

**8**   R \_\_\_\_ \_\_\_\_ U V

# I See

by **Francie Alexander** and **Nancy Hechinger**

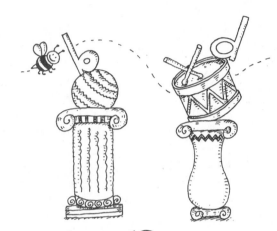

3  I see b.

6  I see d.

9  I see p.

12  I see q.

15  I see b.

18  I see h.

21    I see f.

24    I see t.

27    I see m.

30    I see w.

43    I see the b, d, p, q, h, f, t, m, and w.

47    I see a lot!

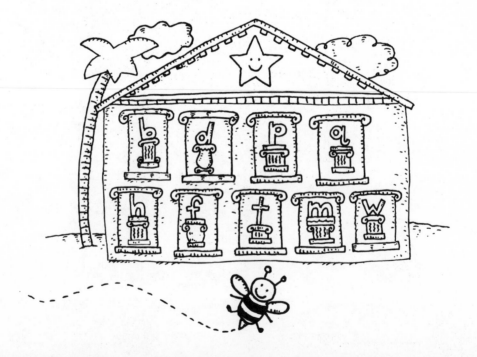

**Fill in the missing letter.**

 _____at

 _____og

 _____ish

 _____en

 _____ig

 _____at

 _____op

 _____ig

# Pop! Pop! Popcorn!

by **Carol Pugliano-Martin**

3    **Popcorn 1:** Pop!

6    **Popcorn 2:** Pop!

10   **Popcorn 3:** Pop! Pop!

14   **Popcorn 4:** Pop! Pop!

19   **Popcorn 5:** Pop! Pop! Pop!

24   **Popcorn 6:** Pop! Pop! Pop!

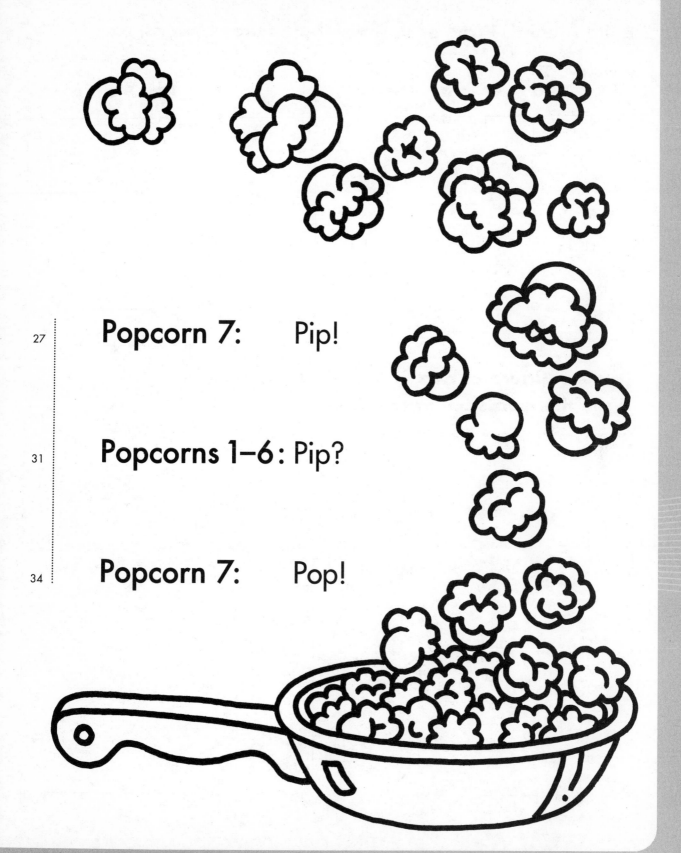

**Popcorn 7:**     Pip!

27

**Popcorns 1–6:** Pip?

31

**Popcorn 7:**     Pop!

34

**Build a word. Write each letter that makes a word.**

|  |  |  |
|---|---|---|
| d | w | h |
| l | m | n |

_____ot  _____ot

_____ot  _____ot

|  |  |  |
|---|---|---|
| f | h | m |
| n | p | t |

_____op  _____op

_____op  _____op

**Draw a picture of two of the words you made.
Write the words under the boxes.**

_____  _____

# Sam Sat

by **Wiley Blevins**

2  Sam sat.

5  Sam got hot.

9  Sam got a hat.

11  Pam sat.

14  Pam got hot.

18  Pam got 2 fans.

20 | Jan sat.

23 | Jan got hot.

29 | Jan got Pam and Sam wet!

**Build a word. Write each letter that makes a word.**

| b | c | s | | f | h | m |
| g | l | m | | z | p | r |

_____at          _____at

_____an          _____an

_____at          _____at

_____an          _____an

**Draw a picture of two of the words you made.**
**Write the words under the boxes.**

_____          _____

# Books I Read

| Book Title | Rating |
|---|---|
| 1. |  |
| 2. |  |
| 3. |  |
| 4. |  |
| 5. |  |

# The Alphabet Forward and Backwards

7   A - B - C - D - E - F - G,

16   H - I - J - K - L - M - N - O - P,

19   Q - R - S,

22   T - U - V,

24   W - X,

27   Y and Z.

32   Now I know my ABCs.

39   Next time sing them backwards with me.

46    Z - Y - X - W - V - U - T

55    S - R - Q - P - O - N - M - L - K

58    J - I - H,

61    G - F - E,

63    D - C,

66    B and A

71    Now I've said my ZYXs.

77    Bet that's not what you expected!

**Fill in the missing letters.**

# A Bug in a Jug

by **Cindy Chapman**

6    A bug is in a jug.

12    A bug is in a mug.

18    A bug is on a rug.

23    I can't hug **this** bug!

29 | A cat is on a mat.

35 | A cat is on a hat.

41 | A cat is on a rat.

46 | I can't pat **this** cat!

**Build a word. Write each letter that makes a word.**

| | | |
|---|---|---|
| b | f | h |
| j | r | w |

_____ug          _____ug

_____ug          _____ug

| | | |
|---|---|---|
| b | f | l |
| r | s | z |

_____un          _____un

_____un          _____un

**Draw a picture of two of the words you made.**
**Write the words under the boxes.**

_____          _____

# I See a Cat

by **Cindy Chapman**

4   I see a cat.

9   I see a big cat.

15   I see a big, fat cat.

24   I see a big, fat cat on a mat.

33   I see a big, fat cat on MY lap!

37    I see a rat.

42    I see a big rat.

48    I see a big, fat rat.

57    I see a big, fat rat on a mat.

68    I will NOT see a big, fat rat on MY lap!

Use the words in the box to finish each sentence.
Write the word on the line.

| | | | | |
|---|---|---|---|---|
| big | mat | sat | see | cat |

**1**  I _____ a little cat.

**2**  The cat is not _____.

**3**  The _____ is black.

**4**  The cat _____ on my lap.

**5**  The cat sat on a _____, too.

# This Is the Way We Go to School

by **Ellen Booth Church**

8    This is the way we go to school,

14    Go to school, go to school.

22    This is the way we go to school.

27    So early in the morning.


33    _____ (name) walks with mom or dad,

39    mom or dad, mom or dad.

45    _____ (name) walks with mom or dad,

50    So early in the morning.

56 _____ (name) rides the yellow school bus,

60 the yellow school bus,

64 the yellow school bus.

70 _____ (name) rides the yellow school bus,

75 So early in the morning.

81 _____ (name) gets a ride to school,

89 a ride to school, a ride to school.

95 _____ (name) gets a ride to school,

100 So early in the morning.

**Read the words under each box.**
**Draw a picture to match the words.**

I see a yellow bus.

I see a red bus.

I go to school.

I sit with my mom.

# Books I Read

| Book Title | Rating |
|---|---|
| **1.** | |
| **2.** | |
| **3.** | |
| **4.** | |
| **5.** | |

# Crab Jab!

by **Cindy Chapman**

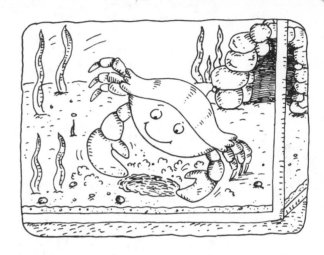

7 **Crab 1:** Dig! Dig! Dig in the

10 sand, sand, sand.

17 **Crab 2:** Run! Run! Run in the

20 sun, sun, sun.

26 **Crab 3:** Grab! Grab! Grab the

29 man, man, man.

35 **Crab 4:** Jab! Jab! Jab his

38 hand, hand, hand!

**Crab 1:** Stop! Stop! Stop! Too hot, 45

hot, hot to grab, dig, jab! 51

**Crab 2:** Swim. Swim. Swim in the 58

wet, wet, wet pond. 62

**Crab 3:** Fan! Fan! Fan in the 69

hot, hot sun. 72

**Crab 4:** Sit! Sit! Sit on the 79

man, man, man. 82

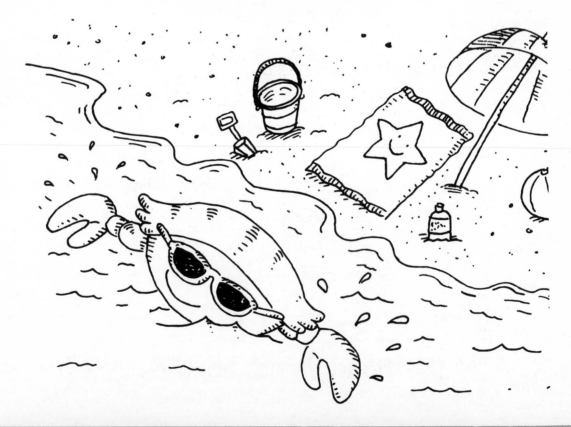

# Comprehension

**Read the words under each box.**
**Draw a picture to match the words.**

I can run.

The sun is hot.

I like to swim.

The man sat.

# A Lot on Top

by **Wiley Blevins**

4   I see the dog.

10   The dog is on the mat.

18   The cat is on top of the dog.

26   The pot is on top of the cat.

34   The mop is on top of the pot.

42   Mom said, "I see a lot on top!"

43   Plop!

# Comprehension

Use the words in the box to finish each sentence.
Write the word on the line.

| | | | | |
|---|---|---|---|---|
| mop | lot | mom | top | dog |

 **1** I have a little, black _____.

 **2** I see a _____ of cats.

 **3** My _____ helps me at home.

 **4** I like to _____ the floor.

 **5** The cat sat on _____ of the hat.

# Will It Fit?

by **Gail Tuchman** and **Anne Schreiber**

6    Will fox fit in the box?

13    A fox CAN fit in the box.

19    "I like the fan," said fox.

29    Will a fan and a fox fit in the box?

39    A fan and a fox CAN fit in the box.

46 "I see a big fish," said fox.

56 Will a fish, fan, and fox fit in the box?

66 A fish, fan, and fox CAN fit in the box.

73 "I see a fat frog," said fox.

81 Will a frog, fish, fan, and fox fit

84 in the box?

85 NO!

91 A frog, fish, fan, and fox

97 can NOT fit in the box!

**Add <u>f</u> to each word part.**
**Draw a picture of the word you made.**

_____ish

_____an

_____ox

_____rog

# Pigs at Bat

7  Bob the pig is up at bat.

12  "I am big," said Bob.

19  "I can hit and we can win!"

20  BAM!

28  "I hit it!" said Bob to the pigs.

33　But the pigs can't win.

35　Why not?

39　Big pigs can bat.

43　Big pigs can hit.

49　But, can big pigs jog fast?

53　No, not a bit!

**Build a word. Write each letter that makes a word.**

| b | d | f |
|---|---|---|
| h | s | v |

_____it            _____it

_____it            _____it

| f | h | p |
|---|---|---|
| t | w | z |

_____in            _____in

_____in            _____in

**Draw a picture of two of the words you made.**
**Write the words under the boxes.**

_____            _____

# 4 Books I Read

| Book Title | Rating |
|---|---|
| **1.** | |
| **2.** | |
| **3.** | |
| **4.** | |
| **5.** | |

# New Frog in the Pond

by **Carol Pugliano-Martin**

5   **Frog 1:** Who are you?

11  **Frog 2:** I am a frog.

18  **Frog 1:** I am a frog, too.

22           Are you new here?

28  **Frog 2:** Yes, I am new.

35  **Frog 1:** Do you like this pond?

44  **Frog 2:** Yes, I like this pond a lot.

**49**    **Frog 1:** Can you hop?

**55**    **Frog 2:** Yes, I can hop.

**62**    **Frog 1:** Show me how you hop.

**67**    **Frog 2:** Hop! Hop! Hop!

**74**    **Frog 1:** You are a good hopper!

**78**    **Frog 2:** Thank you.

**86**    **Frog 1:** Would you like to be friends?

**95**    **Frog 2:** Yes, I would like to be friends.

**100**    **Frog 1:** Let's go hopping.

**105**    **Both Frogs:** Hop! Hop! Hop!

## Comprehension

**Read the question. Circle the letter for the answer.**

 **What can hop?**

  **a.** pigs

  **b.** frogs

  **c.** cats

**For each sentence, find the word that fits. Circle the letter for that word.**

 **Is _____ pond fun?**

  **a.** thin

  **b.** this

  **c.** thank

 **A frog can _____.**

  **a.** hot

  **b.** pop

  **c.** hop

**What is the same about the frogs in the pond?**

_____

_____

## Challenge

Draw pictures of the frogs in the pond. Label each frog as *Frog 1* or *Frog 2*.

# BUNNY HOP

by **Cindy Chapman**

4    **Bunny 1:** I hop!

10    **Bunny 2:** I hop, hop, hop!

17    **Bunny 3:** I hop, hop, and hip!

26    **Bunny 4:** I hip and hop, hip and hop!

**Bunny 5:** I hip and flip, hop and flop!

**Bunny 6:** I hip-hop, flip-flop, hip-hop,

flip-flop!

**Bunny 7:** Stop!

**Bunnies 1–6:** Stop?

**Bunny 7:** No flip! No flop! No flip-flop!

**Bunnies 1–7:** Hip-hop! Hip-hop! Hip

and hop! Hip and hop!

Hop, hop, hop!

35
44
46
49
53
62
70
75
78

**Read the question. Circle the letter for the answer.**

 **How many bunnies hip-hop?**

    **a.** 7

    **b.** 1

    **c.** 6

**For each sentence, find the word that fits. Circle the letter for that word.**

 **I flip and flop _____ hop.**

    **a.** ant

    **b.** and

    **c.** at

 **The bunny can hop to the _____ of the hill.**

    **a.** flop

    **b.** hop

    **c.** top

**Why did the bunny say "Stop!"?**

_____

_____

## Challenge

Draw a picture of one of the bunnies. Then read the part of that bunny as you hold up your picture.

# My Hand Says Hello

4    My hand says hello,

8    My hand says hello,

14    Every time I see my friends,

18    My hand says hello!

22    My eye says hello,

26    My eye says hello,

32    Every time I see my friends,

36    My eye says hello!

40 | My smile says hello,

44 | My smile says hello,

50 | Every time I see my friends,

54 | My smile says hello!

## Comprehension

**Read the question. Circle the letter for the answer.**

 **What says hello?**

    **a.** my toe, my lip, my nose

    **b.** my cat, my pup, my bird

    **c.** my hand, my eye, my smile

**For each sentence, find the word that fits. Circle the letter for that word.**

 **My _____ clap.**

    **a.** man

    **b.** hands

    **c.** fans

 **My eyes can _____.**

    **a.** see

    **b.** beep

    **c.** run

**How can hands say hello? How can eyes say hello?**

_____

_____

## Challenge

Act out "My Hand Says Hello."

# The Red Hen

by **Cindy Chapman**

7  The Red Hen had lots of seeds.

15  The Red Hen saw Dog, Cat, and Duck.

22  "Who will help me plant my seeds?"

29  "Not us," said Dog, Cat, and Duck.

36  "Then I will do it," Hen said.

40  The wheat got tall.

48  The Red Hen saw Dog, Cat, and Duck.

55  "Who will help me cut the wheat?"

62 "Not us," said Dog, Cat, and Duck.

69 "Then I will do it," Hen said.

77 The Red Hen saw Dog, Cat, and Duck.

84 "Who will help me make buns from

91 the wheat? Who will help me bake?"

98 "Not us," said Dog, Cat, and Duck.

105 "Then I will do it," Hen said.

114 "Who will help me eat the buns?" asked Hen.

121 "We will!" said Dog, Cat, and Duck.

128 "No! I will do it," Hen said.

131 And she did!

## Comprehension

**Read the question. Circle the letter for the answer.**

 **What did Hen want?**

   **a.** help making jam

   **b.** help making bread

   **c.** help making friends

**For each sentence, find the word that fits. Circle the letter for that word.**

 **A _____ can swim and fly.**

   **a.** duck

   **b.** sun

   **c.** pup

**3 The _____ can sit on eggs.**

   **a.** ten

   **b.** pen

   **c.** hen

**What is this story about?**

_____

_____

## Challenge

Act out the story by reading each animal's part in a different voice.

# 5 Books I Read

| Book Title | Rating |
|---|---|
| **1.** | |
| **2.** | |
| **3.** | |
| **4.** | |
| **5.** | |

# Max's Pet

by **Nancy Leber** and **Amy Levin**

3    This is Max.

6    Max is six.

13    "Can I get a dog?" said Max.

16    "I like dogs."

23    "Can I get a frog?" said Max.

26    "I like frogs."

33    "Can I get a fish?" said Max.

36    "I like fish."

43    "Can I get a cat?" said Max.

46    "I like cats."

53      "Can I get a pig?" said Max.

56      "I like pigs."

58      No dog.

60      No frog.

62      No fish.

64      No cat.

66      No pig.

68      No pets!

74      But, Max got a big box.

79      A ball was in it.

84      A top was in it.

89      A book was in it.

94      A dinosaur was in it.

98      Max got his pet!

**Read the question. Circle the letter for the answer.**

 **What did Max want?**

   **a.** a pet

   **b.** a home

   **c.** a book

**For each sentence, find the word that fits. Circle the letter for that word.**

 **The _____ naps on my bed.**

   **a.** fat

   **b.** cat

   **c.** sat

**3** **We will _____ a ball at the shop.**

   **a.** set

   **b.** pet

   **c.** get

**Write the names of three pets that Max wanted.**

_____

_____

## Challenge

What gift would you give to Max? Draw a picture of it. Explain why this is a good gift.

# Big Ben and His Ox

6    Big Ben got his big ax.

12    He said to his ox Jane,

22    "I bet I can cut ten logs with my ax!"

29    "I bet I can, too," said Jane.

34    "I am big and strong."

42   "Then let's get set, Jane!" said Big Ben.

51   "I can't get them up the hill by myself."

55   Jane helped Big Ben.

63   "I can. I can. I can," said Jane.

68   "We can!" said Big Ben.

78   Jane and Ben got all ten logs up the hill.

81   They did it!

# Comprehension

**Read the question. Circle the letter for the answer.**

 **1** **What did Jane and Big Ben do?**

   **a.** They made a big cake.

   **b.** They made logs into a home.

   **c.** They got logs up a hill.

**For each sentence, find the word that fits. Circle the letter for that word.**

 **2** **Bill can cut the tree into _____.**

   **a.** hogs

   **b.** mops

   **c.** logs

 **3** **Can the van get up that big _____?**

   **a.** fill

   **b.** hill

   **c.** pin

**How do Jane and Big Ben get the job done?**

_____

_____

## Challenge

Talk about what else Jane and Ben could do by working together.

# The Red Sled

by **Julie Small-Gamby**

6    Bess sat on the red sled.

10    Bess met ten cats.

13    "Get on, cats."

17    Bess met ten hens.

20    "Get on, hens."

24    Bess met ten bats.

27    "Get on, bats."

35    Bess, ten cats, ten hens, and ten bats

40    slid on the red sled.

41    Wheeeeee!

## Comprehension

**Read the question. Circle the letter for the answer.**

 **Where was Bess?**

    **a.** on a sled

    **b.** in a bed

    **c.** in a home

**For each sentence, find the word that fits. Circle the letter for that word.**

 **My mom is in the _____ van.**

    **a.** bed

    **b.** red

    **c.** fed

 **Kim will put on her new _____.**

    **a.** hat

    **b.** sat

    **c.** fat

**What happens last in this story?**

_____

_____

## Challenge

Draw a picture of Bess, the cats, the hens, and the bats on the red sled. Write a sentence about your picture.

# See a Zig-Zag Man

by **Cindy Chapman**

6     See? See a zig-zag man?

17     I see a zig-zag man run a zig-zag mile.

28     I see a zig-zag man put a zig-zag hen

33     on a zig-zag pile.

44   I see a zig-zag man get a zig-zag cat.

55   I see a zig-zag cat smell a zig-zag rat.

67   I see a zig-zag man sit in a zig-zag home

77   with a zig-zag cat and a zig-zag rat.

**Read the question. Circle the letter for the answer.**

 **What is this story about?**

 a. a tan man

 b. a fun pet

 c. a zig-zag man

**For each sentence, find the word that fits. Circle the letter for that word.**

 **Can you zig and _____ in a van?**

 a. flag

 b. bag

 c. zag

 **Jill did not _____ the man.**

 a. beep

 b. week

 c. see

**Write what the zig-zag man likes to do.**

_____

_____

## Challenge

Write other zig-zag pets the zig-zag man will like.

# Books I Read

| Book Title | Rating |
|------------|--------|
| **1.** | |
| **2.** | |
| **3.** | |
| **4.** | |
| **5.** | |

# I Made a Cake

by **Cindy Chapman**

5    I made a big cake.

11    I made a big, BIG cake.

19    I made a big, BIG cake for Dave.

29    I made a big, BIG cake for Dave to save.

34    I gave a big cake.

40    I gave a big, BIG cake.

48    I gave a big, BIG cake to Dave.

58    I gave a big, BIG cake to Dave to save.

63  Dave ate the big cake.

70  Dave ate lots of the big cake.

78  Dave ate lots and LOTS of the cake!

86  Dave did not save the big, BIG cake!

89  I came late.

94  Dave did not save cake.

101  Dave did not save the big cake.

109  Dave did not save the big, BIG cake.

117  Dave did not save the big, BIG cake

120  **that** I made!

126  I will bake a new cake.

**Read the question. Circle the letter for the answer.**

 **What is the story about?**

    **a.** jam

    **b.** cake

    **c.** cars

**For each sentence, find the word that fits. Circle the letter for that word.**

 **Put a lot in the _____.**

    **a.** hot

    **b.** fog

    **c.** pot

 **We can _____ a big cake.**

    **a.** Jake

    **b.** lake

    **c.** make

**Why did Dave eat lots of cake?**

_____

_____

## Challenge

Draw a picture to go with <u>I Made a Cake</u>.

# The Cat and the Rat

by Cindy Chapman

10 A big, big cat put his paw on a little,

12 little rat.

22 "Let me go," said Rat. "I can help a big,

24 big cat!"

34 "How can a little, little rat help a big, big

37 cat?" asked Cat.

43 "I can. I can," said Rat.

51 "OK, I <u>will</u> let you go," said Cat.

59 Rat ran and ran and ran and ran.

69 Then the little, little rat saw the big, big cat

74 in a big, big net!

83 "Help," said the big, big, cat. He was sad!

93 "I can help," Rat said. The little, little rat bit

101 and bit and bit the big, big net!

110 The little, little rat helped the big, big cat!

119 The little, little rat and the big, big cat

121 are friends.

**Read the question. Circle the letter for the answer.**

 **1** **What did the little rat do?**

    **a.** sit on the big cat

    **b.** help the big cat

    **c.** bit the big cat

**For each sentence, find the word that fits. Circle the letter for that word.**

 **2** **Did Pam see the big, fat _____?**

    **a.** dig

    **b.** pig

    **c.** rig

 **3** **A cat has a _____.**

    **a.** saw

    **b.** paw

    **c.** law

**How did the rat free the big cat?**

_____

_____

## Challenge

Act out this tale with a friend.

# The Pancake Man

by **Cindy Chapman** and **Wiley Blevins**

6  Pancake Man hops off the pan.

14  He sees the sun. He runs and runs!

22  He runs and runs to a fat pig.

31  "I will eat you! I am big," says Pig.

37  But Pancake Man runs and runs.

44  "Run, run as fast as you can.

48  You can't get me.

52  I'm the Pancake Man!"

59 Then he sees Sam, a big man.

64 Sam likes to eat pancakes!

71 But Pancake Man just runs and runs.

78 "Run, run as fast as you can.

82 You can't get me.

86 I'm the Pancake Man!"

93 Then he sees a big, red fox.

98 "Pancake Man, sit in this

102 big box!" says Fox.

107 "No one will get you!"

113 Pancake Man runs in the box.

122 Then the fox eats him—the bad, bad fox!

## Comprehension

**Read the question. Circle the letter for the answer.**

 **Why did Pancake Man run?**

   **a.** Pig and Sam want to eat him.

   **b.** Pig and Sam ran and ran.

   **c.** Pancake Man did not run.

**For each sentence, find the word that fits. Circle the letter for that word.**

 **The man ran to the _____ of the hill.**

   **a.** pop

   **b.** top

   **c.** hop

 **Does Meg like to _____ by the lake?**

   **a.** run

   **b.** fun

   **c.** bun

**Why did Pancake Man hop off the pan?**

_____

_____

## Challenge

Retell this tale in your own words.

# Meet Stan

by **Millen Lee**

2  Meet Stan.

6  Stan likes to skate.

8  Stan smiles.

13  He steps in the rink.

15  Stan slides.

17  Stan glides.

21  Stan slides and glides.

23    Stan spins.

25    Stan stops.

29    Stan spins and stops.

34    Sometimes Stan slips and falls.

41    Then he stands up and begins again.

## Comprehension

**Read the question. Circle the letter for the answer.**

 **What does Sam like to do?**

    **a.** run

    **b.** bake

    **c.** skate

**For each sentence, find the word that fits. Circle the letter for that word.**

 **If you begin to _____, stop and do not flop!**

    **a.** pin

    **b.** fin

    **c.** spin

 **I like to glide, so I _____.**

    **a.** hide

    **b.** pile

    **c.** smile

**What is this story about?**

_____

_____

## Challenge

Talk about Stan and what he likes to do.